WELCOME TO THE JOURNEY

OH, THE DEPTH OF THE RICHES BOTH OF THE WISDOM AND KNOWLEDGE OF GOD! HOW UNSEARCHABLE ARE HIS JUDGMENTS AND UNFATHOMABLE HIS WAYS! FOR WHO HAS KNOWN THE MIND OF THE LORD, OR WHO BECAME HIS COUNSELOR?" ...FOR FROM HIM AND THROUGH HIM AND TO HIM ARE ALL THINGS. TO HIM BE THE GLORY FOREVER! AMEN.

ROMANS 11:33-34, 36

God As He Longs For You To See Him

TABLE OF CONTENTS

HOW TO START YOUR OWN SMALL GROUP

The fact that you are even reading this page says a lot about you. It says that you are either one of those people that has to read everything, or it says you are open to God using you to lead a group.

Leading a small group can sound intimidating, but it really doesn't have to be. Think of it more as gathering a few friends to get to know each other better and to have some discussion around spiritual matters.

Here are a few practical tips to help you get started:

1. **PRAY**
   One of the most important principles of spiritual leadership is to realize you can't do this on your own. No matter how long you've been a Christian or been involved in ministry, you need the power of the Holy Spirit. Lean on Him... He will help you.

2. **INVITE SOME FRIENDS**
   Don't be afraid to ask people to come to your group. You will be surprised how many people are open to a study like this. Whether you have 4 of 14 in your group, it can be a powerful experience. You should probably plan on at least an hour and a half for your group meeting.

3. **GET YOUR MATERIALS**
   You will need to get a DVD of the video teaching done by Chip Ingram. You can get the DVD from www.livingontheedge.org. Also, it will be helpful for each person to have their own study guide. You can also purchase those through the website.

4. **BE PREPARED TO FACILITATE**
   Just a few minutes a week in preparation can make a huge difference in the group experience. Each week preview the video teaching and review the discussion questions. If you don't think your group can get through all the questions, select the ones that are most relevant to your group.

5. **LEARN TO SAY "I DON'T KNOW"**
   This series takes on some of the most difficult questions that Christians and non-Christians struggle with. These sessions will spark some lively and spirited discussions. When tough questions come up, it's ok for you to say "I don't know". Take the pressure off. No one expects you to have all the answers.

6. **LOVE YOUR GROUP**
   Maybe the most important thing you bring to the group is your personal care for them. If you will pray for them, encourage them, call them, e-mail them, involve them, and love them, God will be pleased and you will have a lot of fun along the way.

Thank you for your availability. May God bless you as you serve Him by serving others.

HOW TO GET THE MOST OUT OF THIS EXPERIENCE

You are about to begin a powerful journey exploring God's attributes. This powerful series taught by Chip Ingram provides in depth teaching. This series will challenge you and provide very practical help for you and your family.

Listed below are the segments you will experience each week as well as some hints for getting the most out of this experience. If you are leading the group, you will find some additional help and coaching on pages (83).

1. BEFORE GOD

It is important for us to get "before God" and submit ourselves to his truth. During this section you will watch the video teaching by Chip. At the end of the teaching segment, Chip will wrap up the session and help the group dive into discussion.

A teaching outline is provided for each session. As you follow along, write down questions or insights that you can share during the discussion time.

Even though most of the verses will appear on the screen and in your notes, it is a great idea to bring your own Bible each week. It will allow you to make notes in your own Bible and find other passages that might be relevant to that week's study.

2. IN COMMUNITY

We not only grow by listening to God's word, but we grow "in community." The friendship and insights of those in the group will enrich your small group experience. Several discussion questions are provided for your group to further engage the teaching content. Keep the following guidelines in mind for having a healthy group discussion.

- **Be involved.** Jump in and share your thoughts. Your ideas are important, and you have a perspective that is unique and can benefit the other group members.

- **Be a good listener.** Value what others are sharing. Seek to really understand the perspective of others in your group and don't be afraid to ask follow up questions.

- **Be courteous.** People hold strong opinions about the topics in this study. Spirited discussion is great. Disrespect and attack is not. When there is disagreement, focus on the issue and never turn the discussion into a personal attack.

- **Be focused.** Stay on topic. Help the group explore the subject at hand, and try to save unrelated questions or stories for afterwards.

- **Be careful not to dominate.** Be aware of the amount of talking you are doing in proportion to the rest of the group, and make space for others to speak.

- **Be a learner.** Stay sensitive to what God might be wanting to teach you through the lesson, as well as through what others have to say. Focus more on your own growth rather than making a point or winning an argument.

3. ON MISSION
    One reason we get "before God" and live "in community" is so that we can be "on mission". Our faith has an external component. We are called to be salt and light by living out our faith in the real world. This section provides some simple suggestions to help the lesson come to life. Don't ignore them; give them a try!

4. ACTION STEP
    Sometimes at the end of the session you will find an "Action Step". The action steps are not so much about reaching out to others as they are about putting into practice what you are learning. These action steps help you to become "doers" of the word, not just "hearers" of the word.

5. READING ASSIGNMENT FOR NEXT WEEK
    To get the most out of this study you will want to prepare by reading the assigned chapters from the book *God As He Longs For You To See Him*. Make notes as you read the chapters and don't forget to bring your book with you to your small group meetings.

INTRODUCTION
Session One

We're glad you decided to study the character of God. This could be one of the most important studies you have ever done. What's unique about this study is it utilizes three important components. There is a book, a DVD, and a study guide/journal. To get the very most out of this study you will want to use all three.

- **BOOK:** God, As He Longs for You to See Him by Chip Ingram

- **DVD:** Chip Ingram teaches a 15-20 minute lesson on each attribute of God

- **STUDY GUIDE/JOURNAL:** This guide will help you follow along with Chip's teaching. The study guide will also have the group discussion questions and action steps to consider. At the end of the study guide you will find some pages where you can journal your thoughts over the weeks of this study.

"OUR AIM IN STUDYING THE GODHEAD MUST BE TO KNOW GOD HIMSELF BETTER. OUR CONCERN MUST BE TO ENLARGE OUR ACQUAINTANCE, NOT SIMPLY WITH THE DOCTRINE OF GOD'S ATTRIBUTES, BUT WITH THE LIVING GOD WHOSE ATTRIBUTES THEY ARE."

J. I. PACKER

"I KNOW NOTHING WHICH CAN SO COMFORT THE SOUL; SO CALM THE SWELLING BILLOWS OF SORROW AND GRIEF; SO SPEAK PEACE TO THE WINDS OF TRIAL, AS A DEVOUT MUSING UPON THE SUBJECT OF THE GODHEAD."

C. S. LEWIS

BEFORE GOD

WATCH VIDEO **"Introduction"**

What if you have the absolutely wrong perception of God?

> "WHAT COMES INTO OUR MINDS WHEN WE THINK ABOUT
> GOD IS THE MOST IMPORTANT THING ABOUT US."
>
> A.W. TOZER

God wants you to have an accurate view of Him.

Your relationship with God will be based on how you see Him.

Once you get an accurate view of God, it will positively impact every area of your Christian life.

IN COMMUNITY

1. When you think of God's existence, how do you perceive the culture is thinking about him? What do you think other people are thinking about when they ponder God?

2. If you were forced to describe God with one word, what word would you use and why?

3. Share with the group one thing you are hoping to get out of this study.

If you have time, consider discussing the following questions:

4. When you were growing up, what was your view of God and what most shaped your view of God?

5. Over the years, how has your view of God changed? And what caused your view of God to change?

ON MISSION

This week look for an opportunity to have a "God conversation" with someone. It could be someone at the office or in your neighborhood or on an airplane. Pray and ask God to open the door for you to initiate a conversation about God. One easy way to start the conversation is to tell them that you are in a small group study talking about who God is and what he's like. You might be surprised how open people are to talking about God and what they believe about him.

Reading Assignment for Next Week

- Read Chapters 1-3

- Use the journal in this study guide to carry you through the reading assignment.

Reminder

Confidentiality

What is said in the group stays in the group. Let's assure each other that everyone is safe to share.

No pressure

Everyone has the option to pass. In fact it's best not to go in a circle every time to answer questions. Share "popcorn style." Allow people to speak as they are led.

Care for one another

This is not a teaching session as much as it is an opportunity to love and care for others.

Pray for each other during the week

Find ways to check in on people in your group.

SEEING GOD WITH 20/20 VISION

Grandfather in a rocking chair. Cosmic cop. Blind watchmaker.

What's your picture of God? Does He smile down at us with a wink and a nod? Does He wait to pounce when we break his laws? Did He wind up the universe and move on to the next galaxy? Even if it's an empty frame, we all have our own portrait of this entity known more commonly as God.

A. W. Tozer, an American pastor and writer during the 20th century wrote, "What comes into our minds when we think about God is the most important thing about us." Nothing in all your life will impact your relationship with God, your relationship with people, your self-view, your decisions, and your purpose like the way you think of God.

TOOLS FOR LIFE CHANGE

There are two books we recommend that will give additional insight as you continue your journey on the attributes of God. Please consider adding, A.W Tozer's **Knowledge of the Holy** and J.I. Packer's **Knowing God** to your library.

WATCH VIDEO **"Seeing God with 20/20 Vision"**

Lesson learned from chapter one:

What we think about God shapes our whole relationship with him.

Lesson learned from chapter two:

We tend, by a secret law of the soul, to move toward our mental image of God.

Common Errors about God

1. We tend to assume that God is just like us.

"TO WHOM WILL YOU COMPARE? OR WHO IS MY EQUAL?" SAYS THE HOLY ONE. LIFT YOUR EYES AND LOOK TO THE HEAVENS: WHO CREATED THESE? HE WHO BRINGS OUT THE STARRY HOST ONE BY ONE, AND CALLS THEM EACH BY NAME. BECAUSE OF HIS GREAT POWER AND MIGHTY STRENGTH, NOT ONE OF THEM IS MISSING. WHY DO

YOU SAY, O JACOB, AND COMPLAIN, O ISRAEL, "MY WAY IS
HIDDEN FROM THE LORD; MY CAUSE IS DISREGARDED BY
MY GOD?" DO YOU NOT KNOW? HAVE YOU NOT HEARD?
THE LORD IS THE EVERLASTING GOD, THE CREATOR OF
THE ENDS OF THE EARTH. HE WILL NOT GROW TIRED OR
WEARY, AND HIS UNDERSTANDING NO ONE CAN FATHOM.

ISAIAH 40:25-28 (NIV)

A right view of God means He is not like us.

2. We tend to reduce Him to measurable and controllable terms.

3. We tend to overlook the obvious and significant ways that He has revealed Himself to us.

God Reveals Himself Through

- Nature
- His Word
- Jesus

VISION TEST

1. Those who know God have great energy for God.

LOW ENERGY / VAGUE KNOWLEDGE   HIGH ENERGY / CLEAR KNOWLEDGE

2. Those who know God have great thoughts of God.

LOW ENERGY / VAGUE KNOWLEDGE   HIGH ENERGY / CLEAR KNOWLEDGE

3. Those who know God show great boldness for God.

LOW ENERGY / VAGUE KNOWLEDGE   HIGH ENERGY / CLEAR KNOWLEDGE

4. Those who know God have great contentment in God.

|___|___|___|___|___|___|___|___|___|___|

"WHAT COMES INTO OUR MINDS WHEN WE THINK ABOUT GOD IS THE MOST IMPORTANT THING ABOUT US. FOR THIS REASON THE GRAVEST QUESTION BEFORE THE CHURCH IS ALWAYS GOD HIMSELF AND THE MOST PORTENTOUS FACT ABOUT ANY MAN IS NOT WHAT HE AT A GIVEN TIME MAY SAY OR DO, BUT WHAT HE IN HIS DEEP HEART CONCEIVES GOD TO BE LIKE."

A. W. TOZER

IN COMMUNITY

1. Who do you know that has great energy, thoughts, boldness, and/or contentment for God?

2. Share specific ways you are personally getting to know God. What are your best practices that have helped you know God better?

16

3. Have someone from the group read out loud the passage Chip read from Isaiah 40:25-28. What verse or phrase most stands out to you? Why?

4. Which of the four statements from the vision test do you most need to work on? And, what is one practical step you could take to begin to work on that? *(Remember: If you are not comfortable sharing, you can always just say "pass")*

5. Chip said that one of the common errors is that we tend to reduce God to measurable and controllable terms. What are some of the negative by-products of such a view of God?

ACTION STEP

Who is someone you know that has great energy, thoughts, boldness or contentment in God? Consider getting together with them in the next week or two and asking them to share their journey with Christ and how they have come to know God deeply.

Reading Assignment for Next Week

*   Read chapter 4 from the book

THE GOODNESS OF GOD

Session Three

There's an old story about a Chinese gentleman who lived on the border of China and Mongolia. In those days, there was constant conflict along the perimeter. The Chinese man had a beautiful horse, a mare, who one day leaped over the fence, raced down the road, crossed the border, and was captured by the Mongolians. His friends came to comfort him.

"That's bad news," they said sadly.

"What makes you think it's bad news?" asked the Chinese gentleman. "Maybe it's good news."

A few days later the mare came bolting into his corral, bringing with it a massive, snow white stallion. His friends crowded around. "That's good news!" they cried.

"What makes you think it's good news?" he asked. "Maybe it is bad news."

Later that week, his son was riding the stallion, trying to break it. He was thrown off and he broke his leg. The friends came. "That's bad news," they cried.

"What makes you think it is bad news?" asked the Chinese gentleman. "Maybe it's good news."

The next week, war broke out with Mongolia, and a Chinese general came through town drafting all the young men. He took them all and they were all later killed, except for the young man who couldn't go because his leg was broken.

The Chinese gentleman said to his friends, "You see, the things you thought were bad turned out good; and the things you thought were good turned out bad."

If we base our perception of God's goodness on our circumstances rather than His character, our view will always be shortsighted. This week, let's discover what it means to trust the Lord to work all things together for our benefit.

WATCH VIDEO **"The Goodness of God"**

> "WITH THE GOODNESS OF GOD TO DESIRE OUR HIGHEST WELFARE, THE WISDOM OF GOD TO PLAN IT, AND THE POWER OF GOD TO ACHIEVE IT, WHAT DO WE LACK?"

A. W. TOZER

"HE WHO DID NOT SPARE HIS OWN SON, BUT DELIVERED HIM OVER FOR US ALL, HOW WILL HE NOT ALSO WITH HIM FREELY GIVE US ALL THINGS?"

ROMANS 8:32 (NKJ)

"THE GOODNESS OF GOD IS THAT WHICH DISPOSES HIM TO BE KIND, CORDIAL, BENEVOLENT, AND FULL OF GOOD WILL TOWARD MEN. HE IS TENDERHEARTED AND QUICK OF SYMPATHY, AND HIS UNFAILING ATTITUDE TOWARD ALL MORAL BEINGS IS OPEN, FRANK, AND FRIENDLY. BY HIS NATURE, HE IS INCLINED TO BESTOW BLESSEDNESS AND HE TAKES HOLY PLEASURE IN THE HAPPINESS OF HIS PEOPLE."

A.W. TOZER

How Has God Revealed His Goodness?

1. Natural Blessings

2. Through his deliverance (Psalm 107)

3. Jesus

How Do We Respond to God's Goodness?

1. Repent

2. Rest

3. Risk

FOR THE LORD GOD IS A SUN AND SHIELD: THE LORD WILL GIVE GRACE AND GLORY: NO GOOD THING WILL HE WITHHOLD FROM THEM THAT WALK UPRIGHTLY.

PSALM 84:11 (NASB)

1. How has this week's study on God's goodness influenced your view of God?

2. Go around the room and give thanks in one sentence for how God has shown his goodness to you.

3. What risk or step of obedience has God prompted you to take, but have not surrendered to?

4. What is one lie you have believed about God?

5. Read Psalm 31:19-24. What phrase of verse most speaks to you? Why?

ACTION STEP

1. At the back of your study guide/journal you will find your set of "Truth or Lie" cards that Chip talked about. On the front of the card write down any lies you have believed that are contrary to the truth of God's goodness. Then, on the back you will find a definition of God's goodness along with a memory verse. Keep that card with you this next week and review it every morning and every evening.

2. Sometime this week make a gratitude list. Take a few minutes and write out specific ways that God has been good to you.

Reading Assignment for Next Week

   •   Read chapter 5 from the book

THE SOVEREIGNTY OF GOD

Session Four

"I'd like a drink of water with two parts hydrogen and two parts oxygen, please."

"Sorry, that's hydrogen peroxide—not exactly a thirst quencher."

"Okay, how about one with just two parts hydrogen."

"Well, don't sit near someone smoking."

"Why?"

"You'd be inhaling some highly flammable gas. Ever heard of the Hindenburg?"

"How about three parts hydrogen and one part nitrogen, would that sooth my parched throat?"

"No problem."

"Really?

"Yeah, if you like ammonia."

Water is defined as two parts hydrogen and one part oxygen. Regardless of personal preferences, scientific credentials, alternative constructs, distaste, or even disdain, you can't change the building blocks of water. Once altered, you have a very different substance.

In our culture's laboratory of tolerance, people want to mix and match their ideas about God and hope it turns out to be God. For many, the idea of a sovereign, or all-powerful God, cannot be fused with a God who seems to allow free reign on evil. Unfortunately, regardless of personal preferences, scientific credentials, alternative constructs, distaste, or even disdain, you can't change the building blocks of God. Once altered. He ceases to be God.

This week we will discover why tolerance is incompatible with the God portrayed in Scripture. Then we will tackle the apparent contradiction of a God who is both in control and yet permits terror, disaster, and extreme hardship. By the end, we will see why the defining parts of God are both unalterable and trustworthy.

WATCH VIDEO **"The Sovereignty of God"**

Why Worship This God?

Because He...

- is before all things. (Col. 1:17, Ps. 90:2, Rev. 1:8,1 Tim 6:16)

- created all things. (Gen. 1:1, Jn. 1:3, Col. I:16)
- upholds all things. (Heb. 1:3, Col. 1:17)
- is above all things. (Eph. 4:6, Isa. 45:5-12)
- knows all things. (Isa. 46:10, Ps. 1394, 6)
- can do all things. (Jer. 32:27, Lk. 1:37)
- accomplishes all things. (Isa. 14:24; 46:10, Eph. 1:11)
- rules over all things. (Dan. 4:34-35,1 Ch. 29:11-12)
- is in control of all things. (Job 42:2, Rom. 8:28)
    - earthly kings — Pr. 2i:i, Rev. 19:16
    - human events — Dan. 2, 7, Ps. 33:9-11
    - good angels — Col. 1:15-16, Rev. 4:8
    - Satan & bad angels — Job 1:6, Eph. 1:21, Phil. 2:10
    - human decisions — Eph. i:li, Rom. 8:29-30, Acts 2:23; U48

Take some time this week and read these verses in order to get an accurate picture of God's sovereignty.

How has God revealed His sovereignty?

- His titles
- His promises
- History
- Fulfilled prophecy
- The work of Christ

Two questions that come up around the sovereignty of God

1. If God is sovereign and in control, why doesn't he prevent evil, pain and suffering?

2. If God is sovereign over all people and events in history, then doesn't that mean all my choices are just a sham?

_____

_____

_____

OH, THE DEPTH OF THE RICHES OF THE WISDOM AND KNOWLEDGE OF GOD! HOW UNSEARCHABLE HIS JUDGMENTS, AND HIS PATHS BEYOND TRACING OUT! "WHO HAS KNOWN THE MIND OF THE LORD? OR WHO HAS BEEN HIS COUNSELOR?" "WHO HAS EVER GIVEN TO GOD, THAT GOD SHOULD REPAY HIM?" FOR FROM HIM AND THROUGH HIM AND TO HIM ARE ALL THINGS. TO HIM BE THE GLORY FOREVER! AMEN.

ROMANS 11:33-36 (NIV)

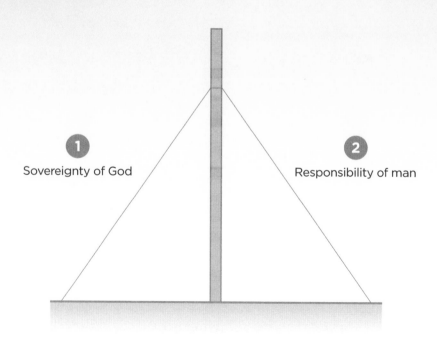

1 Sovereignty of God

2 Responsibility of man

Nothing will ever enter our lives that God doesn't either decree or permit.

But our choices also make a difference and we are responsible for what we do.

Resources to consider:

- *Problem with Pain* by C.S. Lewis
- *Chosen But Free* by Norman Geisler

How do we respond to a sovereign God?

1. Bow before him

   THEREFORE I URGE YOU, BRETHREN, BY THE MERCIES OF GOD, TO PRESENT YOUR BODIES A LIVING AND HOLY SACRIFICE, ACCEPTABLE TO GOD, WHICH IS YOUR SPIRITUAL SERVICE OF WORSHIP.

   ROMANS 12:1 (NASB)

2. Believe all that comes into your life is either allowed or decreed by a good God who will use it for your benefit.

3. Behold in awe the mystery and majesty of this kind, compassionate, just, and sovereign God.

Pull out the Truth or Lie card called the Sovereignty of God from the back of your study guide.

The sovereignty of God is that which separates the God of the Bible from all other religions, truth claims, or philosophies.

When we say God is sovereign, we declare that by virtue of His creatorship, over all life and reality, His all-knowing, all-powerful, and benevolent rule that He is in fact the Lord of all lords, King of all kings, and in absolute control of time and eternity. Nothing will come into my life today that He did not either allow or decree for my ultimate good.

FOR WE KNOW ALL THINGS WORK TOGETHER FOR GOOD
TO THOSE THAT LOVE GOD AND ARE CALLED ACCORDING
TO HIS PURPOSE.

ROMANS 8:28 (NKJ)

YOU MEANT EVIL AGAINST ME BUT GOD MEANT IT FOR
GOOD, IN ORDER TO BRING ABOUT THIS PRESENT RESULT,
TO PRESERVE MANY PEOPLE ALIVE.

GENESIS 50:20 (NASB)

IN COMMUNITY

1. Share a time around the group when you or someone you know experienced a "raw deal" that seemed terrible but ended up really good.

2. From your church or family background, what were you taught about this doctrine?

3. Read Colossians 1:16-18 from a couple of different translations. What do we learn about the supremacy and sovereignty of Christ in this passage?

4. Share one new truth about the sovereignty of God that you've learned through this study.

5. Share one area in your life that you know God wants you to totally surrender. What next steps do you need to take for Him to be the CEO of your life?

ACTION STEP

This week review your Truth or Lie card every morning and evening. Also, if you don't already have Romans 8:28 memorized, work on memorizing it this week.

Reading Assignment for Next Week

- Read chapter 6 from the book

THE HOLINESS OF GOD

One wrong turn can make all the difference.

Have you ever been given a list of directions only to discover at one crossroad you forgot to write down an "R" or an "L"? You have a choice. You can either make a phone call to discover the right way to go. Or, as most of us do, you can make a guess based upon your gut feeling. Unfortunately if we make the wrong turn, just to get back on the right road, we end up taking time, energy, not to mention hearing a slew of "Brilliant! Now you've gone and gotten us lost!"

When we approach the word holy, we have a choice to make. We can pick up the Bible and discover what the word means. Or, as most of us do, we can make a guess based upon our gut feeling of what the word means and how it is applied to God. Unfortunately, if we take the wrong turn, we are absolutely clueless as to what Peter could mean by the phrase, "You shall be holy, for I am holy." Does that mean we need to be perfect? Innocent? Pure? Man, who can travel down that road?

When we say God is holy, or when we say He wants us to be holy, what do we mean? This week we will learn how we have mislabeled "holiness" as it concerns God. Words like perfect, pure, and innocent are good guesses, but in reality they take us down a wrong road in our understanding of God. In our assumptions, we've stripped God of the essence of His holiness. God longs for you to see Him as He is, not as we would want Him to be. This week, let's discover the right turn.

WATCH VIDEO **"The Holiness of God"**

> WE KNOW NOTHING LIKE THE DIVINE HOLINESS. IT STANDS APART, UNIQUE, UNAPPROACHABLE, INCOMPREHENSIBLE, AND UNATTAINABLE. THE NATURAL MAN IS BLIND TO IT. HE MAY FEAR GOD'S POWER AND ADMIRE HIS WISDOM, BUT HIS HOLINESS HE CANNOT EVEN IMAGINE.

A.W. TOZER, KNOWLEDGE OF GOD

The root word of "holy" has in it the idea of "wholeness" and "health."

Three Phases to Holiness

- Justification
- Sanctification
- Glorification

1. Justification = positional holiness
    Positionally, God sees us as holy.

2. Sanctification = practical or progressive holiness
    Practically, in our everyday life we are in a daily battle to become more holy.

3. Glorification = future holiness when we see Jesus
    This is the ultimate holiness where our bodies are glorified and there is no sin and we are in the full presence of God.

How do we respond to God's holiness?

1. It's a commitment we make.

2. It's a way that we think.

Time in God's word and memorizing Scripture are the most powerful ways to reshape your thinking.

1. It's a command we obey.

2. It's an attitude we develop.

"To fear the Lord is to hate evil; I hate pride and arrogance, evil behavior and perverse speech."

PROVERBS 8:13 (NIV)

Holiness is God's means to give you the very best life possible.

Resource to consider:

- *The Miracle of Life Change*
- www.LivingOnTheEdge.org/smallgroup

IN COMMUNITY

1. The two areas people struggle with the most are sex and money. Where do you believe you are at right now?

2. What is the biggest barrier you face today in taking that step of obedience today?

3. Read Galatians 5:16-26. What can you learn from this passage about pursuing personal holiness?

4. Who could help you and hold you accountable to take those steps toward holiness?

_____

_____

_____

ACTION STEP

1. This week tear out the Truth or Lie card called God's Holiness. Write out a lie you have believed about God's holiness. Faithfully review both the truth about God's holiness as well as the scripture passage listed.

2. Take the initiative to pursue that person who can support you and hold you accountable in your pursuit of holiness

Reading Assignment for Next Week

•   Read chapter 7 from the book

THE WISDOM OF GOD

Nothing intrigues us like mystery.

Except when it really happens.

Our eyes leap over pages of a "whodunit." We flock to the big screen when we hear, "You won't believe the ending!" Why? Because we love when a mystery is unveiled and then resolved. Think about the flip side. We let out a moan when the words flash across our favorite TV show, "To be continued." Who likes to leave a stadium in a tie? And that doesn't come close to the feelings that pound us in real-life thrillers:

- As we wait to find out if the chemo treatments will halt the cancer

- As we wonder why the pink slip hit our desk

- As we watch the hurricane move closer to shore

Mystery unveiled: tantalizing.

Mystery unresolved: frustrating.

When theologians describe the simplicity of God, they mean that all of His perfect attributes work perfectly together, in simple harmony. We describe with great clarity His perfect love married with His perfect justice and His perfect holiness. But we trip over our minds when we try to figure out how He is also perfect in His mystery. The preacher of Ecclesiastes asks rhetorically,

> "CONSIDER THE WORK OF GOD, FOR WHO IS ABLE TO STRAIGHTEN WHAT HE HAS BENT?"

ECCLESIASTES 7:13 (NAS)

The picture is one of bare hands trying to straighten curved steel.

What sweat and tears have you lost on trying to straighten out your circumstances? What temples have you rubbed raw trying to figure out how God is going to use this dreadful experience? Surely God can't know about this situation. Doesn't He see how crooked my life is? Why doesn't He straighten it out?

This week we will learn why living in "to be continued" land is not only a necessity, but actually the best thing for us. We will be introduced to another of God's attributes: His wisdom. And that's not about God's IQ. When stuck in your next unresolved mystery remember these principles on how we can learn to rest and trust in the wisdom of God.

WATCH VIDEO "The Wisdom of God"

The Wisdom of God: God brings about the best possible ends, by the best possible means, for the most possible people, for the longest possible time.

- What is the most difficult issue in your life?
- What big problem do you want God to solve?

Imagine what life would be like if you actually believed and applied the definition of wisdom given above.

How Has God Revealed His Wisdom?

1. Creation
2. Providence
3. Redemption
4. Jesus

BE VERY CAREFUL THEN, HOW YOU LIVE—NOT AS UNWISE BUT AS WISE, MAKING THE MOST OF EVERY OPPORTUNITY, BECAUSE THE DAYS ARE EVIL. THEREFORE, DO NOT BE FOOLISH, BUT UNDERSTAND WHAT THE LORD'S WILL IS.

EPHESIANS 5:15-17 (NIV)

Ways to Live a Wise Life

1. Wise living begins with reverence for God.
   Reverence = being afraid.
2. Wise living grows by receiving His Word.
3. Wise living requires that we ask for it specifically.

BUT IF ANY OF YOU LACKS WISDOM, LET HIM ASK OF GOD, WHO GIVES TO ALL GENEROUSLY AND WITHOUT REPROACH, AND IT WILL BE GIVEN TO HIM. BUT HE MUST ASK IN FAITH WITHOUT ANY DOUBTING, FOR THE ONE WHO DOUBTS IS LIKE THE SURF OF THE SEA, DRIVEN AND TOSSED BY THE WIND.

JAMES 1:5- 6 (NASB)

4. Wise living involves learning to trust God completely.

God's agenda is not our happiness; God's agenda is our holiness.

IN COMMUNITY

1. What is the toughest issue you're facing in your life right now (that you feel safe enough to share)?

2. What did you learn about God's wisdom that gave you hope or comfort?

3. What practical steps are you currently taking to gain God's wisdom? What are your best practices?

4. Read Proverbs 2:1-11. As a group make a list of the benefits of wisdom. Then, share which one speaks most to you and your life circumstances.

5. Read Proverbs 9:1-18. What are some lessons we can learn about wisdom and foolishness from this passage? If you could pass on to your child or grandchild a proverb from chapter 9, which one would it be and why?

ACTION STEP

Every day this week ask God for wisdom (James 1:5-6) and then pray this simple prayer:

O Lord God, infinite in wisdom and knowledge, as I consider your purposes and your plans, grant that I might live in total awe and reverence for you, feast daily upon your Word, ask for your wisdom in every situation, and trust you completely when life doesn't make sense.

Let me know your will and help me to follow it whole-heartedly, remembering that you already know every ripple of every action throughout history, now and forever. Because of your wisdom, you freely offer your best in every situation, and you provide it to all who ask. So today, I ask. In Jesus name, Amen.

**Don't forget to review your Truth or Lie cards each day.

Reading Assignment for Next Week

- Read chapter 8 from the book

THE JUSTICE OF GOD

Session Seven

Have you ever seen a dog with a shock collar?

Once he strays outside predetermined boundaries, the collar shocks, the dog yelps, and the masochistic among us chuckle.

He breaks the law. He receives immediate justice. Wouldn't it be nice if that would work in our world? Let's rephrase that: Wouldn't it be nice if that would work in our world for everyone except me? Instead, it appears so many dogs are running loose.

We wonder about God's justice when we hear of the missionary family who moves to an unreached tribe only for the mom to contract a terminal disease. And on the flip side, our fairness needle pushes to the limit when we think about the thugs of society getting off scot-free and in the process, driving a Corvette. Our skeptical preacher in Ecclesiastes laments,

> "I HAVE SEEN EVERYTHING DURING MY LIFETIME OF FUTILITY; THERE IS A RIGHTEOUS MAN WHO PERISHES IN HIS RIGHTEOUSNESS AND THERE IS A WICKED MAN WHO PROLONGS HIS LIFE IN HIS WICKEDNESS"

ECCLESIASTES 7:15 (NAS)

Someone has said, "God must love wicked people, because He puts up with so many of them." We all have heard that God is both just and fair, but this week we will ask why, in our world, bad things happen to good people, and what's even more frustrating, good things happen to bad people. We then learn some practical ways to relax when we wonder why God allows so many dogs to run loose.

WATCH VIDEO "The Justice of God"

By his nature God is fair and righteous and just.

In a fallen world, we don't always get to experience God's justice.

God has repeatedly revealed his justice

1. In the natural order

2. In the human heart

3. In the Bible

4. In the cross

For Christ also died for sins once for all, the just for the unjust, so that He might bring us to God, having been put to death in the flesh, but made alive in the spirit;

1 PETER 3:18 (NAS)

5. In divine retribution

When Christ died on the cross he paid for the sins of all people for all time. God made every human being on the face of the earth "savable". But each person by faith needs to receive that free gift. For those who reject that free gift there will be divine judgment.

How Do We Respond to God's Justice?

1. Choose to embrace Jesus.

"Truly, truly, I say to you, he who hears My word, and believes Him who sent Me, has eternal life, and does not come into judgment, but has passed out of death into life."

JOHN 5:24 (NASB)

2. Refuse to seek vengeance.

3. Take comfort in God's justice.

4. Meditate on the effects of God's final judgment.

1. Share a time when you've questioned God's justice. Either in your life or in a person you love.

    _____

    _____

    _____

2. What did you learn about God's justice in this study to help you cope in the midst of the situation?

    _____

    _____

    _____

3. Which of the four responses to God's justice resonates with you in your life right now? Why?

    _____

    _____

    _____

4. Read Psalm 73:1-17. What insights can you gain from this passage about justice?

    _____

    _____

    _____

5. Is there a specific action step you need to take in response to God's justice? If so, write it down and then share it with the group or a close friend.

ACTION STEP

This week meditate several times on Romans 12:17-21. That is the passage that is on the back of your Truth or Lie card for this week.

> DO NOT REPAY ANYONE EVIL FOR EVIL. BE CAREFUL TO DO WHAT IS RIGHT IN THE EYES OF EVERYBODY. IF IT IS POSSIBLE, AS FAR AS IT DEPENDS ON YOU, LIVE AT PEACE WITH EVERYONE. DO NOT TAKE REVENGE, MY FRIENDS, BUT LEAVE ROOM FOR GOD'S WRATH, FOR IT IS WRITTEN: "IT IS MINE TO AVENGE; I WILL REPAY," SAYS THE LORD. ON THE CONTRARY: "IF YOUR ENEMY IS HUNGRY, FEED HIM; IF HE IS THIRSTY, GIVE HIM SOMETHING TO DRINK. IN DOING THIS, YOU WILL HEAP BURNING COALS ON HIS HEAD." DO NOT BE OVERCOME BY EVIL, BUT OVERCOME EVIL WITH GOOD.

ROMANS 12:17-21 (NIV)

Reading Assignment for Next Week

- Read chapter 9 in the book

THE LOVE OF GOD

You know what happens when you leave soda out on the counter for a few hours.

Overexposure leads to flatness.

The same thing happens with the word love. Love. I love shopping. I love burgers. I love my team. I love that song. I love my bride. I love my kids. I love my dog. Overexposure leads to flatness.

The word love is like a conversational Swiss army knife—perfect for any situation. We apply it as easily to cooked cow as we do our groom of 50 years. We use it affectionately for our daughters and ardently for our favorite football team.

What does God's love look like? Feel like? Has its flavor fallen flat on you? For many of us, we react to the knowledge of God's love as we do the tax code—a cold fact of life. Especially those of us who have been in the church for any length of time, the mantra "God loves you" moved from humbling to humdrum years ago.

God wants to move us back from flat to flavorful. We will come to realize that most of the problem stems from our lack of belief in His love. We know it in our mind, but never feel it in our heart. In the process we will discover five truths of what God's love means for us that will not only change how we view God's love, but may change how we love others.

> "THE CHANGE OF WHICH I SPEAK IS THE CHANGE FROM LIVING LIFE AS A PAINFUL TEST TO PROVE THAT YOU DESERVE TO BE LOVED, TO LIVING IT AS AN UNCEASING "YES" TO THE TRUTH OF THAT BELOVEDNESS."
>
> HENRY NOUWEN

WATCH VIDEO "The Love of God"

Five Distinct Implications of God's Love

1. God's thoughts, intentions, desires and plans are always for your good and never for your harm. Jer. 29:11; James 1:17

2. God is kind, open, approachable, frank, and eager to be your friend. John 13:12-15

3. God emotionally identifies with your pain, joy, hopes, and dreams and has chosen to allow your happiness to affect His own. John 11:33-36

4. He takes pleasure in you just for who you are totally apart from your performance and/or accomplishments. Psalm 139; Zeph. 3; Romans 5:8

THE LORD YOUR GOD IS WITH YOU, HE IS MIGHTY TO SAVE.
HE WILL TAKE GREAT DELIGHT IN YOU, HE WILL QUIET YOU
WITH HIS LOVE, HE WILL REJOICE OVER YOU WITH SINGING.

ZEPH. 3:17 (NIV)

5. God is actively and creatively orchestrating people, circumstances, and events to express His affection and selective correction to provide for your highest good.

Definition of God's Love

God's love is His holy disposition toward all that He has created that compels Him to express unconditional affection and selective correction to provide the highest quality of existence, both now and forever, for the object of His love.

God loves me so much He gives me what I need the most when I deserve it the least at great personal cost to Himself.

How has God objectively proven His love to you?

1. Through Creation

2. Through Providence

3. Through the Incarnation

4. Through Discipline

5. Through the Holy Spirit

6. Through His Son

How do we respond to God's Love?

- We must receive
- We must believe

Three ways to take the love of God from your head down into your heart.

1. Renew your mind
2. Pray and ask God to help
3. Refuse cheap substitutes

IN COMMUNITY

1. Share a time when you've felt deeply loved by God. Why?

2. What is your biggest barrier in believing and receiving God's love for you?

3. Read Ephesians 3:14-21. How is this prayer different than most prayers you hear from Christians?

4. If you really grasped the love of God as described in Ephesians 3, how would you live differently?

5. What specific steps of faith/obedience are you going to take to help you experience and enjoy God's unconditional love for you?

ON MISSION

There are people you interact with every day who have never personally experienced the love of God. Take the challenge this week of praying for people you know who need to experience the love of Christ. Call them by name and intercede on their behalf.

Reading Assignment for Next Week

•   Read chapter 10 of the book

THE FAITHFULNESS OF GOD

Session Nine

The second law of thermodynamics states:

The total entropy of any thermodynamically isolated system tends to increase over time, approaching a maximum value.

And all God's people said, "Huh??" In English: Everything in the universe is gradually deteriorating. Practically speaking, that means light bulbs burn out. Batteries run down. Cars rust out. Bodies wear out. Friends move away. Homes fall apart. And we put caskets in the ground.

It appears so much of our time is spent replacing, maintaining, preventing, and mourning. If everything is in a state of deterioration, what in this world can we count on to remain the same?

Nothing created. But it appears the second law of thermodynamics doesn't apply to the Creator. He never burns out, runs down, rusts out, wears out, moves away, falls apart, or dies. Biblically we call Him the Alpha and the Omega, the beginning and the end, the One who was, and is, and is to come. In a word, faithful. God's faithfulness can be defined as His constant and "loyal love" for us.

Max Lucado writes about God's faithful love to us:

Father. Your love never ceases. Never. Though we spurn you, ignore You, disobey You, You will not change. Our evil cannot diminish Your love. Our goodness cannot increase it. Our faith does not earn it anymore than our stupidity jeopardizes it. You don't love us less if we fail. You don't love us more if we succeed.

This week we will discover why God is the only Person in the universe we can count on. His faithfulness has been revealed through the centuries. His faithfulness bolsters us with hope when the repair bills come in, the mirror stops flattering, and tombstones dot the landscape of our lives.

> GREAT IS THY FAITHFULNESS, O GOD MY FATHER THERE IS NO SHADOW OF TURNING WITH THEE; THOU CHANGEST NOT, THY COMPASSIONS THEY FAIL NOT; AS THOU HAST BEEN THOU FOREVER WILT BE.

"GREAT IS THY FAITHFULNESS" BY THOMAS CHISHOLM

WATCH VIDEO "The Faithfulnenss of God"

God is 100% faithful to His Word, His promises, His people, and His character because He cannot be otherwise. He will never let you down!

How does God reveal His faithfulness?

1. Through His creation

2. Through His people

3. Through His Spirit

4. Through His character

5. Through His Word

6. Through His Son

The faithfulness of God in shaping our lives

1. God demonstrates His faithfulness when we are weak.

2. God reveals His faithfulness when we're tempted.

3. God longs to show His faithfulness to us when we sin.

> IF WE CONFESS OUR SINS, HE IS FAITHFUL AND RIGHTEOUS TO FORGIVE US OUR SINS AND TO CLEANSE US FROM ALL UNRIGHTEOUSNESS.
>
> ———————————————————————
>
> 1 JOHN 1:9 (NASB)

4. God wants to show us His faithfulness even when we utterly fail.

1. What one thing from the past do you need to release?

2. What current pain, problem, or failure do you need to bring Him today?

3. In what specific ways does God reveal his faithfulness through creation?

4. As a group brainstorm a list of times in Scripture that God did what he promised?

5. In what ways have you personally seen the faithfulness of God in your life?

ACTION STEP

This week spend some time reflecting on the words of the great hymn Great Is Thy Faithfulness. You might even want to sing this as a personal prayer to the Lord.

> "GREAT IS THY FAITHFULNESS," O GOD MY FATHER, THERE IS NO SHADOW OF TURNING WITH THEE; THOU CHANGEST NOT, THY COMPASSIONS, THEY FAIL NOT AS THOU HAST BEEN THOU FOREVER WILT BE.
>
> "GREAT IS THY FAITHFULNESS!" "GREAT IS THY FAITHFULNESS!" MORNING BY MORNING NEW MERCIES I SEE; ALL I HAVE NEEDED THY HAND HATH PROVIDED "GREAT IS THY FAITHFULNESS," LORD, UNTO ME!

"GREAT IS THY FAITHFULNESS" BY THOMAS CHISHOLM

TIME TO REMEMBER

Session Ten

"Papa, Papa," said the boy as he yanked on his grandfather's tunic, "what are these stones for?"

"Ah," leaning down, the grandfather pulled his grandson close, "let me tell you a story."

If the children of Israel forgot about the parting of the Red Sea, they would forget about God's power. If the children of Israel forgot about manna dropping from heaven, they would forget about God's provision. If the children of Israel forgot about the fire by night and the cloud by day, they would forget about His faithful presence.

So God asked them to set up some stones:

Now when all the nation had finished crossing the Jordan, the Lord spoke to Joshua, saying, "Take for yourselves twelve men from the people, one man from each tribe, and command them, saying, 'Take up for yourselves twelve stones from here out of the middle of the Jordan, from the place where the priests feet are standing firm, and carry them over with you and lay them down in the lodging place where you will lodge tonight.'" So Joshua called the twelve men whom he had appointed from the sons of Israel, one man from each tribe; and Joshua said to them, "Cross again to the ark of the Lord your God into the middle of the Jordan, and each of you take up a stone on his shoulder, according to the number of the tribes of the sons of Israel. Let this be a sign among you, so that when your children ask later, saying 'What do these stones mean to you?' then you shall say to them,

> 'BECAUSE THE WATERS OF THE JORDAN WERE CUT OFF BEFORE THE ARK OF THE COVENANT OF THE LORD; WHEN IT CROSSED THE JORDAN, THE WATERS OF THE JORDAN WERE CUT OFF' SO THESE STONES SHALL BECOME A MEMORIAL TO THE SONS OF ISRAEL FOREVER."

JOSHUA 4:1-7 (NIV)

Over 40 times in the Bible, God tells his people to "remember." We are a people prone to short term memory loss. If we don't establish memorial stones in the landscape of our mind, we are apt to return to lies, misperceptions, and a fuzzy view of God.

This week, it's time to set up some stones. Ask yourself, "how has my view of God changed?" More importantly, "how has it changed me?" God longs for you to see Him clearly. Let's plan on remembering the view from here on.

WATCH VIDEO "Time to Remember"

"DO NOT LET YOUR HEART BE TROUBLED; BELIEVE IN GOD, BELIEVE ALSO IN ME. IN MY FATHER'S HOUSE ARE MANY DWELLING PLACES; IF IT WERE NOT SO, I WOULD HAVE TOLD YOU; FOR I GO TO PREPARE A PLACE FOR YOU. IF I GO AND PREPARE A PLACE FOR YOU, I WILL COME AGAIN AND RECEIVE YOU TO MYSELF, THAT WHERE I AM, THERE YOU MAY BE ALSO. AND YOU KNOW THE WAY WHERE I AM GOING." THOMAS SAID TO HIM, "LORD, WE DO NOT KNOW WHERE YOU ARE GOING, HOW DO WE KNOW THE WAY?" JESUS SAID TO HIM, "I AM THE WAY, AND THE TRUTH, AND THE LIFE; NO ONE COMES TO THE FATHER BUT THROUGH ME. IF YOU HAD KNOWN ME, YOU WOULD HAVE KNOWN MY FATHER ALSO; FROM NOW ON YOU KNOW HIM, AND HAVE SEEN HIM."

JOHN 14:1-7 (NASB)

PHILIP SAID TO HIM, "LORD, SHOW US THE FATHER, AND IT IS ENOUGH FOR US." JESUS SAID TO HIM, "HAVE I BEEN SO LONG WITH YOU, AND YET YOU HAVE NOT COME TO KNOW ME, PHILIP? HE WHO HAS SEEN ME HAS SEEN THE FATHER; HOW CAN YOU SAY, 'SHOW US THE FATHER'? DO YOU NOT BELIEVE THAT I AM IN THE FATHER, AND THE FATHER IS IN ME? THE WORDS THAT I SAY TO YOU I DO NOT SPEAK ON MY OWN INITIATIVE, BUT THE FATHER ABIDING IN ME DOES HIS WORKS. BELIEVE ME THAT I AM IN THE FATHER AND THE FATHER IS IN ME; OTHERWISE BELIEVE BECAUSE OF THE WORKS THEMSELVES.

JOHN 14:8-11 (NASB)

TRULY, TRULY, I SAY TO YOU, HE WHO BELIEVES IN ME, THE WORKS THAT I DO, HE WILL DO ALSO; AND GREATER WORKS THAN THESE HE WILL DO; BECAUSE I GO TO THE FATHER. WHATEVER YOU ASK IN MY NAME, THAT WILL I DO, SO THAT THE FATHER MAY BE GLORIFIED IN THE SON. IF YOU ASK ME ANYTHING IN MY NAME, I WILL DO IT.

JOHN 14:12-14 (NASB)

ACTION STEP

Retake the Vision Test

1. Those who know God have great energy for God.

LOW ENERGY / VAGUE KNOWLEDGE   HIGH ENERGY / CLEAR KNOWLEDGE

2. Those who know God have great thoughts of God.

LOW ENERGY / VAGUE KNOWLEDGE   HIGH ENERGY / CLEAR KNOWLEDGE

3. Those who know God show great boldness for God.

LOW ENERGY / VAGUE KNOWLEDGE   HIGH ENERGY / CLEAR KNOWLEDGE

4. Those who know God have great contentment in God.

LOW ENERGY / VAGUE KNOWLEDGE   HIGH ENERGY / CLEAR KNOWLEDGE

Now celebrate with each other!

MY JOURNAL

Use the pages of this journal to write out....

- Reflections on what you are learning

- Prayers to God

- What you sense God is saying to you

- What you are thinking and feeling

- Praise and gratitude

SMALL GROUP LEADER RESOURCES

GROUP AGREEMENT

People come to groups with a variety of different expectations. The purpose of a group agreement is simply to make sure everyone is on the same page and that we have some common expectations.

The following Group Agreement is a tool to help you discuss specific guidelines during your first meeting. Modify anything that does not work for your group, then be sure to discuss the questions in the section called Our Game Plan. This will help you to have an even greater group experience!

WE AGREE TO THE FOLLOWING PRIORITIES

- **Take the Bible Seriously** — To seek to understand and apply God's truth in the Bible

- **Group Attendance** — To give priority to the group meeting (Call if I am going to be absent or late.)

- **Safe Environment** — To create a safe place where people can be heard and feel loved (no snap judgments or simple fixes)

- **Respectful Discussion** — To speak in a respectful and honoring way to our mate and others in the group

- **Be Confidential** — To keep anything that is shared strictly confidential and within the group

- **Spiritual Health** — To give group members permission to help me live a godly, healthy spiritual life that is pleasing to God

- **Building Relationships** — To get to know the other members of the group and pray for them regularly

- **Prayer** — To regularly pray with and for each other

- **Other**

  _____

  _____

OUR GAME PLAN

- What will we do for refreshments?

  _____

  _____

  _____

- What will we do about childcare?

  _____

  _____

  _____

- What day and time will we meet?

  _____

  _____

  _____

- Where will we meet?

  _____

  _____

  _____

- How long will we meet each week?

  _____

  _____

  _____

BEFORE THE GROUP ARRIVES

1. **Be prepared.** Your personal preparation can make a huge difference in the quality of the group experience. We strongly suggest previewing both the DVD teaching by Chip Ingram and the study guide.

2. **Pray for your group members by name.** Ask God to use your time together to touch the heart of every person in your group. Expect God to challenge and change people as a result of this study.

3. **Provide refreshments.** There's nothing like food to help a group relax and connect with each other. For the first week, we suggest you prepare a snack, but after that, ask other group members to bring the food so that they share in the responsibilities of the group and make a commitment to return.

4. **Relax.** Don't try to imitate someone else's style of leading a group. Lead the group in a way that fits your style and temperament. Remember that people may feel nervous showing up for a small group study, so put them at ease when they arrive. Make sure to have all the details covered prior to your group meeting, so that once people start arriving, you can focus on them.

BEFORE GOD (Watch the Video)

1. **Get the video ready.** Each video session on the DVD will be about 20 minutes in length. Chip will not only do the teaching but he will set up the discussion time for your group. Most often Chip will ask you as the leader to start off the discussion. It's important for you as the leader to model authenticity.

2. **Test the equipment.** Be sure to test your video equipment ahead of time and make sure you have located this week's lesson on the DVD menu. The video segments flow from one right into the next. So, once you start the session, you won't have to stop the video until Chip has finished his closing thoughts and prepared the group for the first discussion question.

3. **Have ample materials.** Before you start the video, also make sure everyone has their own copy of the study guide/journal. Encourage

the group to open to this week's session and follow along with the teaching. There is an outline in the study guide that makes it easy to follow the teaching.

4. **Arrange the room.** Set up the chairs in the room so that everyone can see the television. And, arrange the room in such a way that it is conducive to discussion.

IN COMMUNITY

Here are some guidelines for leading the discussion time:

1. **Make this a discussion, not a lecture.** Resist the temptation to do all the talking, and to answer your own questions. Don't be afraid of a few moments of silence while people formulate their answers.

   And don't feel like you need to have all the answers. There is nothing wrong with simply saying "I don't know the answer to that, but I'll see if I can find an answer this week".

2. **Encourage everyone to participate.** Don't let one person dominate, but also don't pressure quieter members to speak during the first couple of sessions. Be patient. Ask good follow up questions and be sensitive to delicate issues.

3. **Affirm people's participation and input.** If an answer is clearly wrong, ask "What led you to that conclusion?" or ask what the rest of the group thinks. If a disagreement arises, don't be too quick to shut it down! The discussion can draw out important perspectives, and if you can't resolve it there, offer to research it further and return to the issue next week.

   However, if someone goes on the offensive and engages in personal attack, you will need to step in as the leader. In the midst of spirited discussion, we must also remember that people are fragile and there is no place for disrespect.

4. **Detour when necessary.** If an important question is raised that is not in the study guide, take time to discuss it. Also, if someone shares something personal and emotional, take time for them. Stop and pray for them right then. Allow the Holy Spirit room to maneuver, and follow his prompting when the discussion changes direction.

5. **Subgroup.** One of the principles of small group life is "when numbers go up, sharing goes down". So, if you have a large group, sometimes you may want to split up into groups of 4-6 for the discussion time. This is a great way to give everyone, even the quieter members, a chance to share. Choose someone in the group to guide each of the smaller groups through the discussion. This involves others in the leadership of the group, and provides an opportunity for training new leaders.

6. **Prayer.** Be sensitive to the fact that some people in your group may be uncomfortable praying out loud. As a general rule, don't call on people to pray unless you have asked them ahead of time or have heard them pray in public. But this can also be a time to help people build their confidence to pray in a group. Consider having prayer times that ask people to just say a word or sentence of thanks to God.

ON MISSION

These simple suggestions will help the group be "on mission". These *On Mission* applications are outward focused. They help your group members care about and engage those who don't know Christ. There will not be an On Mission component every week. Be sure and leave adequate time to talk about these practical applications of the lesson.

ACTION STEP

Most of these assignments involve an action step that will encourage the group to put into practice what they are learning. Occasionally ask people if they have been working on these assignments and what the results have been.

READING ASSIGNMENT FOR NEXT WEEK

Chip's book *God As He Longs For You To See Him* is an integral part of this study. In the video Chip will refer to the book often and ask people to turn to various sections and follow along with something Chip reads. So, it is important that each group member have a book. And, it will be important for you to encourage people to keep up with the reading each week.

SESSION NOTES

Thanks for hosting this series called *God As He Longs For You To See Him*. This practical series will help you get a clear and accurate picture of God. Whether you are brand new at leading a small group or you are a seasoned veteran, God is going to use you. God has a long history of using ordinary people to get his work done.

These brief notes are intended to help prepare you for each week's session. By spending just a few minutes each week previewing the video and going over these leader notes you will set the table for a great group experience. Also, don't forget to pray for your group each week.

Session 1: Introduction

- If your group doesn't know each other well, be sure that you spend some time getting acquainted. Don't rush right into the video lesson. Remember, small groups are not just about a study or a meeting, they are about relationships.

- Be sure to capture everyone's contact information. It is a good idea to send out an e-mail with everybody's contact information so that the group can stay in touch. At the back of your study guide is a roster where people can fill in the names and contact information of the other group members.

- When you are ready to start the session, be sure that each person in your group has a copy of the book and study guide/journal. The small group study guide is important for people to follow along and to take notes.

- The video lesson taught by Chip Ingram will be about 20 minutes in length. So, you will have plenty of time for discussion.

- At the end of each session Chip will set up the discussion questions and will usually ask you as the leader to go first in getting the discussion started. This allows you to lead by example and your willingness to share openly about your life will help others feel the permission to do the same.

- In your study guide on page 84 is a Group Agreement followed by Our Game Plan. The Group Agreement is a simple way to make sure that everyone understands the ground rules for how you will do your group. Take just a few minutes to review this with your group and have everybody agree to these priorities.

Session 2: Seeing God with 20/20 Vision

- Why not begin your preparation by praying right now for the people in your group. You might even want to keep their names in your Bible. You may also want to ask people in your group how you can pray for them specifically.

- If somebody doesn't come back this week, be sure and follow up with them. Even if you knew they were going to have to miss the group meeting, give them a call or shoot them an e-mail letting them know that they were missed. It would also be appropriate to have a couple of other people in the group let them know they were missed.

- If you haven't already previewed the video, take the time to do so. It will help you know how to best facilitate the group and what are the best discussion questions for your group.

- As Chip talked about in the first session, no one needs to feel pressured to share. So be sensitive about calling on people, especially people who might be new to the group. And, reinforce Chip's coaching by letting people know that they can always just say "pass" when they don't want to share.

Session 3: The Goodness of God

- Did anybody miss last week's session? If so, make it a priority to follow up and let them know they were missed. It just might be your care for them that keep them connected to the group.

- Share the load. One of the ways to raise the sense of ownership within the group is to get them involved in more than coming to the meeting. So, get someone to help with refreshments... find somebody else to be in charge of the prayer requests... get someone else to be in charge of any social gathering you plan... let someone else lead the discussion one night. Give away as much of the responsibility as possible. That is GOOD leadership.

- This week Chip introduces the Truth or Lie cards. This is a great tool for really changing our thinking. A set of perforated cards is included at the back of your study guide/journal. You might even have group members go ahead and tear them out as Chip talks about these. Also, be sure to check in each week and see how people are doing with reviewing the cards.

- In this session Chip will share the Gospel. It would be good for you to let your group know that you are available if anyone has questions or wants to talk further about what it means to have a personal relationship with Jesus Christ.

- At the end of this week's session Chip will encourage you to try subgrouping for the prayer time. In other words, instead of having everyone stay together for the prayer time, break the group up into smaller groups of 2-4 and have them pray together.

Session 4: God's Sovereignty

- Don't feel any pressure to get through all the questions. As people open up and talk, don't move on too quickly. Give them the space to what is going on inside them as they interact with this teaching.

- Don't be afraid of silence. When you ask people a question, give them time to think about it. Don't feel like you have to fill every quiet moment with words.

- Confidentiality is crucial to group life. The moment trust is breached; people will shut down and close up. So, you may want to mention the importance of confidentiality again this week just to keep it on people's radar.

- This week's lesson on the Sovereignty of God can be a challenging one. People have a wide variety of understanding and opinion about this doctrine. Be careful not to let the group spend all their time chasing rabbits. Remember to major on the majors.

Session 5: The Holiness of God

- As you start this week's session, do a check in on how people are doing with applying the Action Step. Also, find out how people are doing with using their Truth or Lie cards.

- Think about last week's meeting for a moment. Was there anyone that didn't talk or participate? In every group there are extroverts and there are introverts. There are people who like to talk and then there are those who are quite content NOT to talk. Not everyone engages in the same way or at the same level, but you do want to try and create an environment where everyone wants to participate.

- If you have a mixed group of men and women, Chip is going to ask them to separate for the discussion time. The nature of this week's content and questions will make it more appropriate to the men and women separate for the discussion.

Session 6: The Wisdom of God

- You are now at the halfway point of this series. How is it going? How well is the group connecting? What has been going well and what needs a little work? Are there any adjustments you need to make?

- One way to deepen the level of community within your group is to spend time together outside the group meeting. If you have not already done so, plan something that will allow you to get to know each other better. Also, consider having someone else in the group take responsibility for your fellowship event.

- As you begin this week's session, do a check-in to see what people are learning and applying from this series. Don't be afraid to take some time at the beginning of your meeting to review some key ideas from the previous week's lessons.

- During the discussion time this week you are going to read a couple of lengthy passages from Proverbs. You might want to have a couple of extra Bibles on hand. Also, consider reading these passages from a couple of different translations. That will provide a fresh angle on the same verses.

Session 7: The Justice of God

- Consider asking someone in your group to facilitate next week's lesson. Who knows, there might be a great potential small group leader in your group. It will give you a break and give them a chance to grow.

- Consider sending an e-mail to each person in your group this week letting them know you prayed for them today. Also, let them know that you are grateful that they are in the group.

- Take a few minutes this week before you get into the study to talk about the impact of this series so far. Ask people what they are learning, applying, and changing in their lives. For this series to have lasting impact it has to be more than just absorbing information. So, challenge your group to put what they are learning into action.

- This week's lesson on the Justice of God is a heavy topic. During the discussion time this week people will be asked to share time when they questioned God's justice. There could be some very personal sharing this week. So, take adequate time to allow people to share. Be prayed up and follow the leading of the Holy Spirit.

Session 8: The Love of God

- Follow up questions. The only thing better than good questions are good follow up questions. Questions are like onions. Each question allows another layer to be peeled back and get beneath the surface.

- In your group meetings be sure to take adequate time for prayer. Don't just tack it on at the end of the meeting simply out of obligation. Also, don't be afraid to stop the meeting and pray for someone who shares a need or a struggle.

- During this session Chip will again talk about the gospel and invite people to receive Christ. If people want to explore salvation Chip tells them to ask someone in group or ask your pastor how to take the step of receiving Christ. So, be prepared to follow up with those in your group.

- This week there is an On Mission assignment. The assignment is to pray for those around us who have not yet experienced the love of Christ. You might want to include this as part of your group prayer time

Session 9: The Faithfulness of God

- Since this is the next to the last week of this study, you might want to spend some time this week talking about what your group is going to do after you complete this study. Chip is going to challenge a person or two from your group to lead this same study with some of their friends.

- As this series winds down, this is a good time to plan some kind of party or fellowship after you complete the study. Find the "party person" in your group and ask them to take on the responsibility of planning a fun experience for the group. Also, use this party as a time for people to share how God has used this series to grow them and change them.

- As Chip closes the session this week he will say that there may be some things going on with people that they don't feel comfortable sharing with the group. He will encourage them to go see their pastor or a very close friend or a Christian counselor. As the group leader, encourage them to take the next step in order to get the help and healing they need.

- During this session Chip will also encourage you to have a good season of prayer together. So, be sure to leave adequate time for the group to pray together.

- This week is largely about celebration. Chip's teaching will be brief as he walks you through John 14. You might want to plan for a meal together and some extended time to talk. Be sure to celebrate the specific learning and impact that this series has had on the people in your group.

- Be sure that everyone is clear what your group is doing next after this study.

PRAYER AND PRAISE

One of the most important things you can do in your group is to pray with and for each other. Write down each other's concerns here so you can remember to pray for these requests during the week!

Use the Follow Up box to record an answer to a prayer or to write down how you might want to follow up with the person making the request. This could be a phone call, an e-mail, or a card. Your personal concern will mean a lot!

DATE	PERSON	PRAYER REQUEST	FOLLOW UP

DATE	PERSON	PRAYER REQUEST	FOLLOW UP

DATE	PERSON	PRAYER REQUEST	FOLLOW UP

DATE	PERSON	PRAYER REQUEST	FOLLOW UP

GROUP ROSTER

NAME	HOME PHONE	EMAIL

What's Next?

Small Group Studies offered by Chip Ingram and Living on the Edge.

GOD: AS HE LONGS FOR YOU TO SEE HIM

How would you describe God? Awesome? All Powerful? Creator? While we cannot know Him exhaustively, we can know Him truly. And God longs for you to see Him as He truly is. Join Chip in this fascinating series studying the seven attributes of God.

MIRACLE OF LIFE CHANGE

Is life change really possible? If we're honest most of us would answer, "No." You've tried numerous programs that promise big changes, but in reality, deliver very little results. You long for transformation, but don't know where to begin. There's good news for you and there is hope. Life change is possible!

r12: LIVING ON THE EDGE

Being a genuine disciple of Christ flows out of a relationship with Him. It's about experiencing God's grace, not earning His love through performance. A real relationship with Jesus Christ will produce a follower whose life looks progressively more like His life. Romans 12 provides a relational profile of an authentic disciple: someone who is surrendered to God, separate from the world's values, sober in self-assessment, serving in love and supernaturally responding to evil with good. Christians who live out this kind of lifestyle are what we call r12 Christians.

EFFECTIVE PARENTING IN A DEFECTIVE WORLD

Raising children is a tough challenge in today's world. Peers and pop culture exert a never-ending pressure on kids. Many come from split homes. But the good news is that God has been working with people from bad situations for a long time! In Effective Parenting you will learn how God's principles for raising children still work today. Packed with practical advice, this series will give struggling parents a vision for their children's future and life-changing help for today!

WHY I BELIEVE

An apologetic series to address your "honest doubts" and most pivotal questions about the claims of the Christian faith - What Happens When We Die? Can Miracles Be Explained? Is There Really A God? Answers to questions such as these are as varied as they are confusing and spring from a plethora of mystical belief systems. But the facts, we can know the truth. There are solid, logical answers to satisfy the heart and the mind of those who are seeking.

EXPERIENCING GOD'S DREAM FOR YOUR MARRIAGE

Would you like a fresh breeze to blow in your marriage? Do you long for a marriage where intimacy and communication are a reality instead of a dream? "Experiencing God's Dream for Your Marriage" is a topical series by Chip Ingram examining God's design for marriage, with practical instruction to help you make your marriage what God desires it to be.

FIVE LIES THAT RUIN RELATIONSHIPS

Have you ever looked back over a situation or relationship in your life and wondered how it became so messy or difficult? In Five Lies that Ruin Relationships, we'll define five of the most common lies that have the potential to ruin relationships with those we love. What we think about life determines how we live it, so there is power in knowing and applying God's truth when confronted with lies and discovering the freedom He longs for us to enjoy in our relationships.

LOVE, SEX & LASTING RELATIONSHIPS

Everyone wants to love and be loved. The pursuit of "true love" is everywhere you look! It's romanticized on TV and in the movies we watch. There are books about it, songs about it, internet dating, and even seminars on it... all of which are designed to "help" you find that special someone to love. So why is "true love" so elusive? Could it be that the picture of love we see in today's culture is nothing more than an illusion? If so, what does real love look like? In this series, you'll discover that there is a better way to find love, stay in love, and grow in intimacy for a lifetime. Chip Ingram delivers to us God's prescription for building relationships that last a lifetime.

BALANCING LIFE'S DEMANDS

Are you busy, tired, stressed out, and stretched to the limit? Does life seem a little out of control? Are you running long on "to do's" and short on time? If so, join us in this series, Balancing Life's Demands. You'll learn how to put "first things first" and find peace in the midst of pressure and adversity. No clichés or quick fixes, just practical biblical insights to help you order your personal world.

REBUILDING YOUR BROKEN WORLD

Lives today are filled with pain. Either through stress, pressure, unfortunate circumstances or bad decisions, many of us find ourselves living in a world that has fallen apart. This series from James 1 is designed to help you begin where you are and rebuild your broken world.

INVISIBLE WAR

Beneath our tangible landscape lurks an invisible spiritual realm where an unseen battle rages. It's real and it's dangerous. If you're prepared to remove the blinders and gaze into the unseen world, Chip is ready to take you there.

To Order: LivingontheEdge.org or call 888-333-6003

GOD'S GOODNESS

*Lies I believe about
God's goodness...*

_____
_____
_____
_____
_____
_____
_____
_____

GOD'S SOVEREIGNTY

*Lies I believe about
God's sovereignty...*

_____
_____
_____
_____
_____
_____
_____
_____

GOD'S HOLINESS

*Lies I believe about
God's holiness...*

_____
_____
_____
_____
_____
_____
_____
_____

GOD'S WISDOM

*Lies I believe about
God's wisdom...*

_____
_____
_____
_____
_____
_____
_____
_____

DEFINITION OF GOD'S SOVEREIGNTY

The sovereignty of God is that which separates the God of the Bible from all other religions, truth claims, or philosophies.

When we say God is sovereign, we declare that by virtue of His creatorship over all life and reality, His all-knowing, all powerful, and benevolent rule, that He is in fact the Lord of all lords, King of kings, and in absolute control of time and eternity. Nothing will come into my life today that He did not either allow or decree for my ultimate good.

AND WE KNOW THAT GOD CAUSES ALL THINGS TO WORK TOGETHER FOR GOOD TO THOSE WHO LOVE GOD, TO THOSE WHO ARE CALLED ACCORDING TO HIS PURPOSE.

ROMANS 8:28

AS FOR YOU, YOU MEANT EVIL AGAINST ME, BUT GOD MEANT IT FOR GOOD IN ORDER TO BRING ABOUT THIS PRESENT RESULT, TO PRESERVE MANY PEOPLE ALIVE.

GENESIS 50:20

DEFINITION OF GOD'S GOODNESS

The goodness of God is that which disposes Him to be kind, cordial, benevolent, and full of good will toward men. He is tender-hearted and of quick sympathy, and His unfailing attitude toward all moral beings is open, frank, and friendly. By His nature He is inclined to bestow blessedness and He takes total pleasure in the happiness of His people.

FOR THE LORD GOD IS A SUN AND SHIELD; THE LORD GIVES GRACE AND GLORY; NO GOOD THING DOES HE WITHHOLD FROM THOSE WHO WALK UPRIGHTLY.

PSALM 84:11

DEFINITION OF GOD'S WISDOM

THE WISDOM OF GOD TELLS US THAT GOD WILL BRING ABOUT THE BEST POSSIBLE RESULTS, BY THE BEST POSSIBLE MEANS, FOR THE MOST POSSIBLE PEOPLE, FOR THE LONGEST POSSIBLE TIME.

DR. CHARLES RYRIE

OH, THE DEPTH OF THE RICHES BOTH OF THE WISDOM AND KNOWLEDGE OF GOD! HOW UNSEARCHABLE ARE HIS JUDGMENTS AND UNFATHOMABLE HIS WAYS! FOR WHO HAS KNOWN THE MIND OF THE LORD, OR WHO BECAME HIS COUNSELOR? OR WHO HAS FIRST GIVEN TO HIM THAT IT MIGHT BE PAID BACK TO HIM AGAIN? FOR FROM HIM AND THROUGH HIM AND TO HIM ARE ALL THINGS TO HIM BE THE GLORY FOREVER. AMEN.

ROMANS 11:33-36

DEFINITION OF GOD'S HOLINESS

WE KNOW NOTHING LIKE THE DIVINE HOLINESS. IT STANDS APART, UNIQUE, UNAPPROACHABLE, INCOMPREHENSIBLE AND UNATTAINABLE. THE NATURAL MAN IS BLIND TO IT. HE MAY FEAR GOD'S POWER AND ADMIRE HIS WISDOM, BUT HIS HOLINESS HE CANNOT EVEN IMAGINE. ONLY THE SPIRIT OF THE HOLY ONE CAN IMPART TO THE HUMAN SPIRIT THE KNOWLEDGE OF THE HOLY.

A. W. TOZER

AS OBEDIENT CHILDREN, DO NOT BE CONFORMED TO THE FORMER LUSTS WHICH WERE YOURS IN YOUR IGNORANCE, BUT LIKE THE HOLY ONE WHO CALLED YOU, BE HOLY YOURSELVES ALSO IN ALL YOUR BEHAVIOR; BECAUSE IT IS WRITTEN, "YOU SHALL BE HOLY, FOR I AM HOLY"

I PETER 1:14-16